Live Like Grunt

Written by **Nikki Burdine**
and **Miles Burdine**

Illustrated by **Teresa Wilkerson**

For Andi. I love you bigger than the world.

Live Like Grunt
Written by Nikki Burdine and Miles Burdine
Illustrated by Teresa Wilkerson
Book Design by Tara Sizemore
Published November 2020
Skippy Creek
Imprint of Jan-Carol Publishing, Inc

Copyright © Nikki Burdine and Miles Burdine
ISBN: 978-1-950895-68-7
Library of Congress Control Number: 2020949698

You may contact the publisher:
Jan-Carol Publishing, Inc.
PO Box 701
Johnson City, TN 37605
publisher@jancarolpublishing.com
www.jancarolpublishing.com

Jan-Carol
Publishing, Inc
"every story needs a book"

To the Reader

Live Like Grunt is a story about a yellow lab who gave the Burdine family unconditional love and loyalty for about a dozen years. Grunt was his name and love was his game. Miles and Denise Burdine brought Grunt home for their three girls, Nikki, Laura, and Alyce. His name came from Miles, who is a USMC Colonel, also known as a "Grunt." They do the hard work, the dirty work, the groundwork...the Grunt work. Grunt Dog also adorably grunted quite a bit as a puppy.

Grunt followed the girls wherever they went, did whatever they did, and was always happy to do so. The feeling was mutual. But the girls slowly learned, it was Grunt's attitude that was worth emulating.

Miles created a daily "Thoughts by Grunt Dog" email he sent out to his girls. The 'thoughts' were often accompanied by a picture of Grunt Dog and a quote. This book is a collection of "Thoughts by Grunt Dog" that make for great life lessons for any family.

When you're happy,
dance around
and wag your tail.

If you want friends,
wag your tail,
not your tongue.

No matter how often you're scolded,
don't pout and feel sorry for yourself...

...run right back and make friends.

Be loyal.

Regardless of how stupid the words of a friend or family member may sound, look at them as if it's the most amazing thing you've ever heard.

It's important to
be a good listener.

When someone is having a bad day,
be silent, sit close to them,
and nuzzle and cuddle them gently.

Always let your family
know that you love them,
even when you're mad.

Never stop learning,
no matter your age.

Always be yourself.
You're the only you
out there!

Delight in the simple things in life.

Be persistent and never
give up on your dreams.
(Eventually they will drop food!)

Patience is a virtue.

Eat with enthusiasm. Stop when you've had enough.

Love is like bacon,
there's no such thing
as too much.

Time with your loved ones
is better than any toy.

Never underestimate
the comfort of
a cold, wet nose.

Face challenges head-on.

Actions speak louder than words.

Do something every day
that challenges and scares you.

On warm days, stop to lie on your back in the grass.

Don't judge others who look different.
Remember, it's what's inside that counts.

Don't bite when a growl will do.

Never pass up the opportunity
to go for a joyride.

At all costs, regardless of the risk, protect your family.

Live Like Grunt

About the Authors

Nikki Burdine is a mom, wife, and a morning television journalist. She lives in Nashville with her daughter Andi, husband Justin, cat Louis, and dog Reggie White. Nikki has worked in TV news in Maryland, Kentucky, Washington, D.C., and Tennessee since 2007, covering some of the nation's biggest stories. She received an Emmy for her work while reporting in Washington, D.C. She is a graduate of the University of Tennessee, Knoxville with a degree in journalism. Follow Nikki on Instagram: Nikki Burdine, and on her website, NikkiBurdine.com, which is also where this book can be purchased.

Miles Burdine is the ultimate Girl Dad to three girls: Nikki, Laura, and Alyce. He and his wife, Denise, are the proud grandparents to two girls: Andi and Ada. A graduate of the University of Tennessee with a degree in Business Administration, Miles is the CEO of the chamber of commerce in Kingsport, Tennessee. Miles' other career is with the United States Marine Corps. Having served 30 years and now retired at the rank of Colonel, three of his deployments were to combat environments: Beirut, Lebanon in 1983; Operation Desert Shield/Desert Storm in Saudi Arabia in 1991, and Operation Iraqi Freedom in 2005/2006. Accomplishing his mission, keeping his Marines safe and returning to see "My Girls" kept Miles focused and positive during each deployment.

CPSIA information can be obtained
at www.ICGtesting.com
Printed in the USA
LVHW021110251120
672528LV00001B/1